D0236401

THE BEANO BOOK 1987

Printed and Published in Great Britain by D. C. THOMSON & CO., LTD.,
185 Fleet Street, London EC4A 2HS.
© D. C. THOMSON & CO., LTD., 1986.
**ISBN** 0 85116 360 2

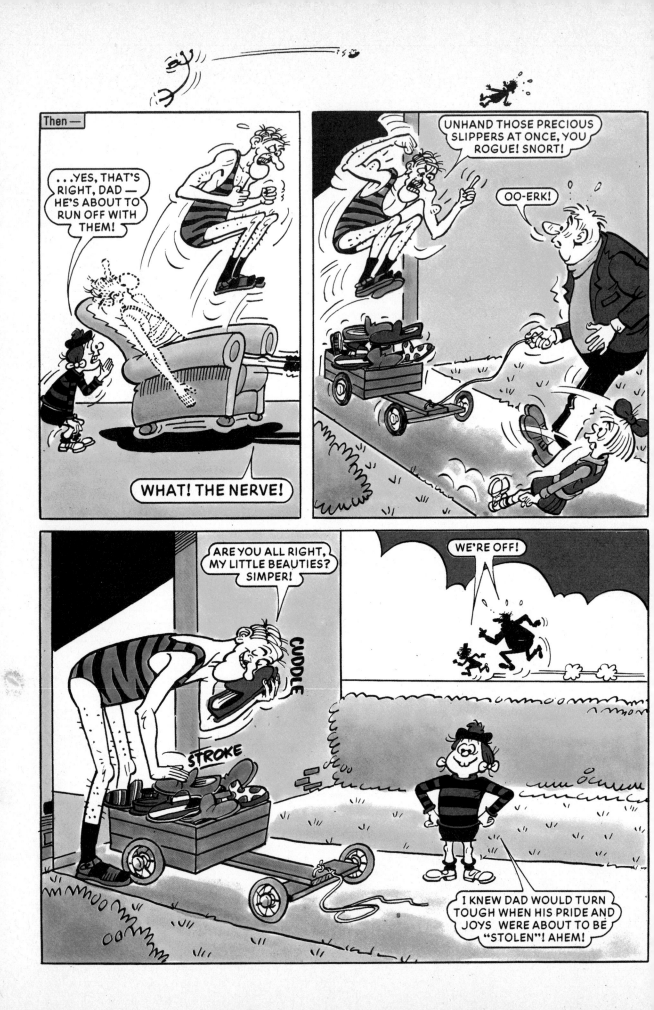

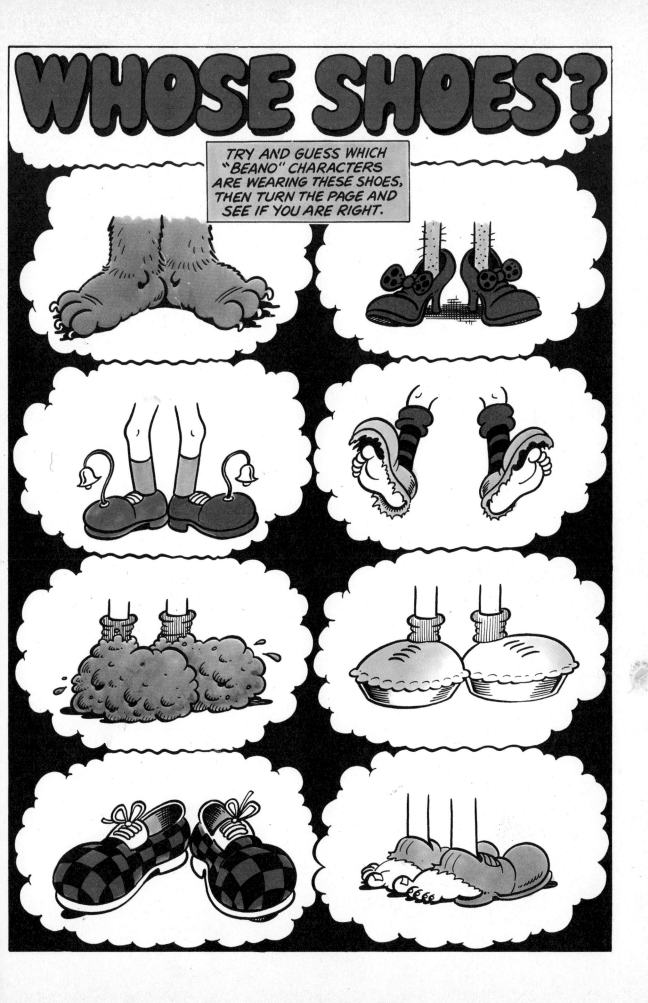

# BEANO FACT-FILES

R

NAME — Roger The Dodger.

AGE — Difficult to say — sometimes has more than one birthday a year to get more presents.

HEIGHT — 1.06 metres when he is bending down to dodge the slipper and 2.32 metres when he's stretching up to pinch apples.

AMBITION — To earn a living without working — like the "Beano" Editor!

FAVOURITE FILM — "Oliver Twist" with my hero, the Artful Dodger!

FAVOURITE OTHER "BEANO" CHARACTER — Smudge — he's always dodging baths!

FAVOURITE PLACE — Dodge City.

# BEANO FACT-FILES

## B

NAMES — Danny, Smiffy, Plug, Fatty, Toots, Sidney, 'Erbert, Spotty and Wilfred.

AGE — 78 years added together. (164¾ if you count Teacher!)

HEIGHT — 13.67 metres, standing on each others shoulders.

FAVOURITE COLOUR — Tartan (only way we could get all our favourite colours together!)

AMBITIONS — Being a film star, climbing Mount Everest, playing for Wham!, eating the largest tuck hamper in the world, scoring the winning goal in the Cup Final, being the heavyweight champion of the world, driving the fastest car, being the fastest runner ever, and also to be the women's tennis champion! (The last one is Toots's ambition!)

TEACHER'S AMBITION — To see that lot fulfil their ambitions and LEAVE ME IN PEACE!

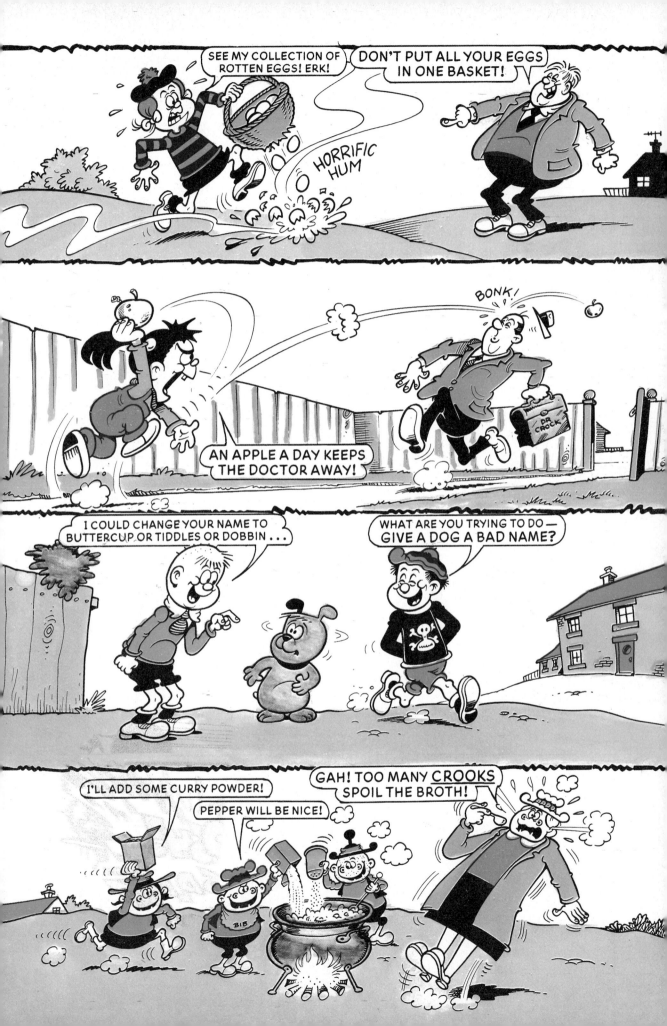

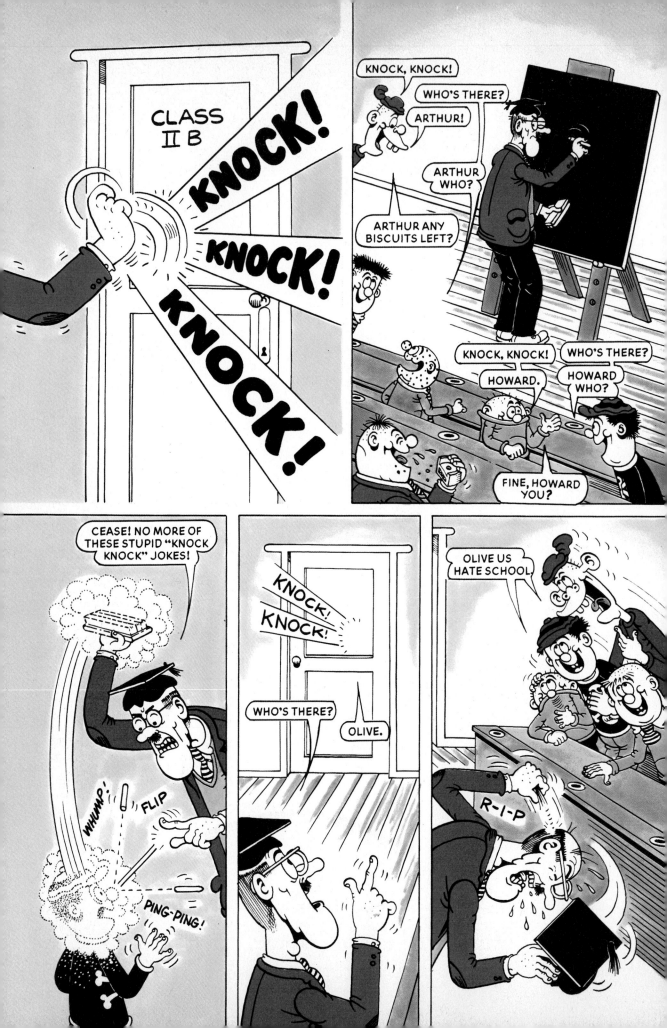

# RHYME
## BASH STREET VERSIONS

It is an ancient Mariner
And he stoppeth one of three.
'By thy long grey beard and glittering eye,
Now wherefore stopp'st thou me?
Samuel Taylor Coleridge

It is an ancient Teacher,
Who drinketh Olive's tea.
"By thy grey hair and
Bloodshot eye,
Why dost thou poison me?"

I wander'd lonely as a cloud
That floats on high o'er vales and hills,
When all at once I saw a crowd,
A host, of golden daffodils;
William Wordsworth

I wandered lonely as a cloud,
That floats on high o'er vale and hill,
The reason is I've skipped off school
Pretending that I'm ill.

Shall I compare thee to a hulking ape?
Thou art more ugly and more strange of shape,
You make the green leaves wither on the bough,
Please place a bucket o'er your head right now.

Shall I compare thee to a Summer's day?
Thou art more lovely and more temperate:
Rough winds do shake the darling buds of May,
And Summer's lease hath all to short a date:
William Shakespeare

Dinner, dinner, burning bright,
Flames leap high, my, what a sight.
Olive's food is now alight.
Cooking salad isn't right!

Tiger, Tiger, burning bright
In the forests of the night,
What immortal hand or eye
Could frame thy fearful symmetry?
William Blake

# TIME
## OF FAMOUS POEMS

O my luve's like a red, red rose
That's newly sprung in June:
O my luve's like
The melodie
That's sweetly played in tune!
Robert Burns

My Teacher sniffed a red, red rose,
That grows near our classroom,
Now Teacher's got a red, red nose,
A bee lurked in the bloom.

O to be in England
Now that April's there,
And whoever wakes in England
Sees, some morning,
Unaware,
Robert Browning

Oh to be in Bash Street,
Now that April's there,
For now's the time birds
build their nests,
In Toots and Sidney's hair.

The Kids and a pussy cat went
to sea in a beautiful
pea green boat.
As Fatty had just eaten
lunch,
The vessel failed to
float.

The Owl and the
Pussycat went to
sea
In a beautiful
pea green boat,
They took some
honey, and plenty
of money,
Wrapped up in a
five pound note.
Edward Lear

Under the spreading
chestnut tree
The Silly Smiffy
stands,
With his best gloves
upon his feet,
And wellies on his
hands.

Under a spreading
chestnut tree
The village smithy
stands;
The smith, a mighty
man is he,
With large and
sinewy hands,
Henry Wadsworth
Longfellow

# BEANO FACT-FILES

NAME — Smudge.

HEIGHT — Exactly the same as a hippopotamus sunk up to its knees in mud.

WEIGHT — 37 kilos when cleaned — at least 5 times that when muddy.

HAIR COLOUR — Depends what kind of muck I've been playing in.

FAVOURITE SPORT — Swimming — never in water though (yuck!) — only in mud.

AMBITION — To live in a mud hut in the middle of a mud flat miles away from Mum and soap. Also to find out what my pet, Spludge, is.

FAVOURITE TV PROGRAMME — Don't know. My TV's been covered in mud for years.

FAVOURITE CLOTHES — Ones that haven't been washed for a month — except in mud!

FAVOURITE COLOUR — Need you ask?

FAVOURITE FOOD — Oxtail soup, eaten with fingers, of course.

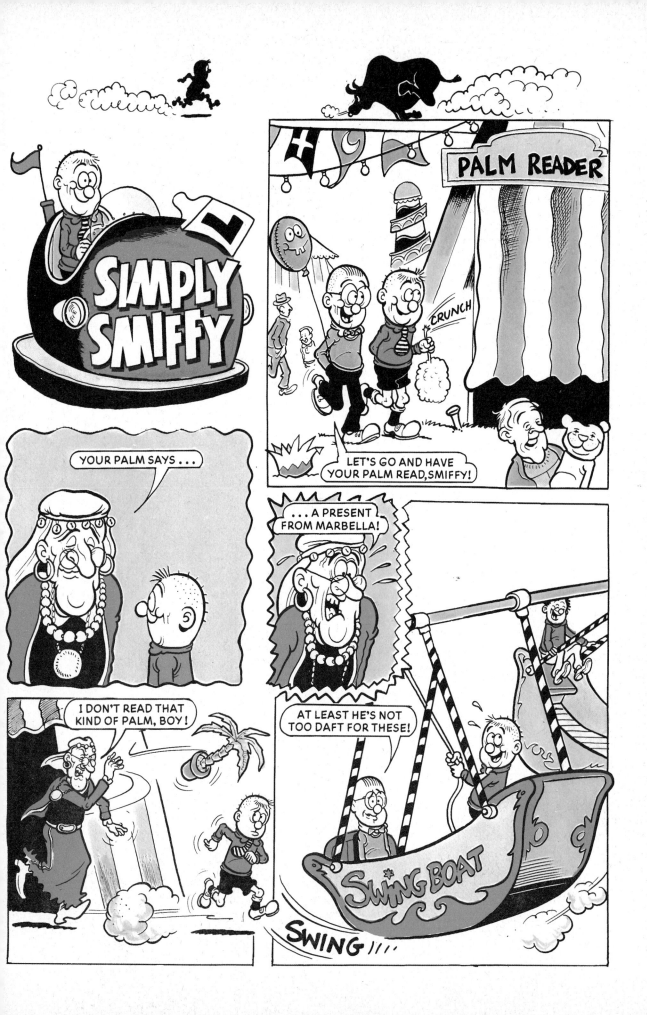

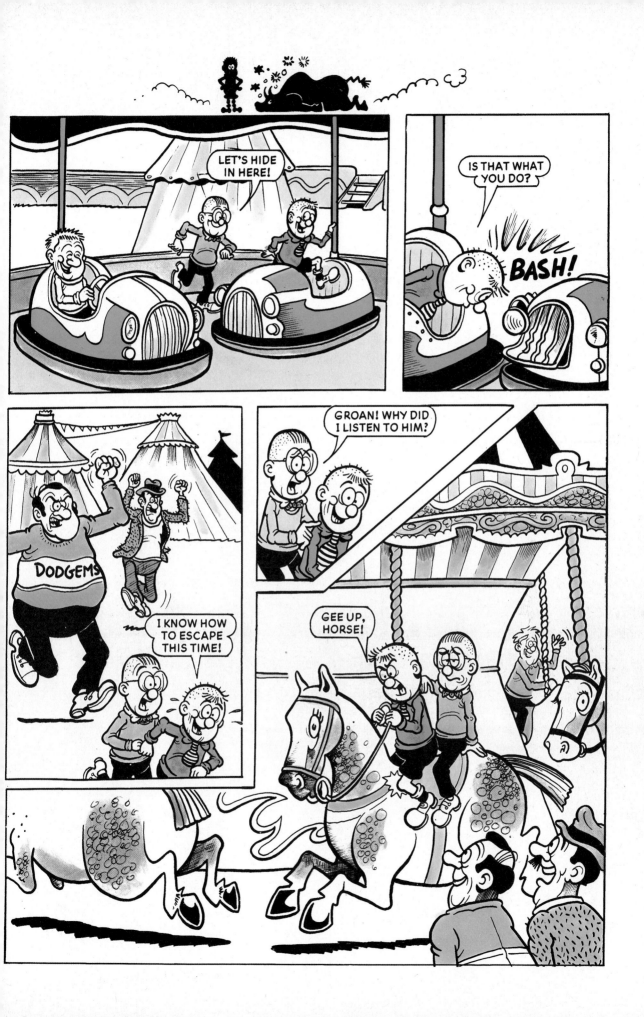

# BEANO FACT-FILES

M

NAME — Minnie the Minx.

OCCUPATION — Terrorising Dad and everyone else!

WEIGHT — FIGHTING WEIGHT — 34 kilos.

AFTER MY FAVOURITE TEA (6 fish suppers, 3 arctic rolls and a large bottle of limeade!)

WEIGHT — 84 kilos.

WHAT DO YOU WANT TO BE WHEN YOU GROW UP? — Tougher!

CAR — A souped-up soap box GMX (Grand Minx) with all the extras — flour bombs, selection of water pistols, pea-shooters and catapults!

FAVOURITE TV PROGRAMME — All-in wrestling.

But I'm still waiting for my invite to fight Big Daddy AND Giant Haystacks at the same time!

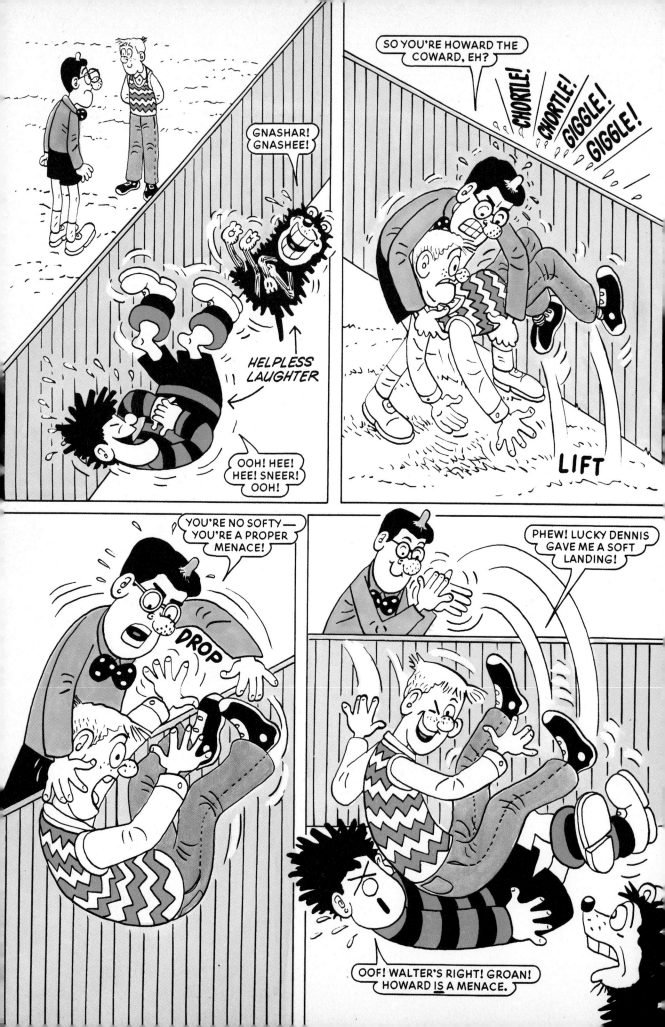

# BEANO FACT-FILES

D+G

NAMES — Dennis and Gnasher.

OCCUPATION — Menaces.

FAVOURITE SPORT — Menacing Softies.

FAVOURITE FOOD — Curries and bones (Er — not on the same plate, though).

WHAT DO YOU WANT TO BE WHEN YOU GROW UP? — An astronaut, a fighter pilot, top dog at Crufts (Gnasher — not Dennis!), a footballer, and Dad's boss — all at once!

SUPERSTITIONS — Never let a Softy cross your path without menacing him!

BIGGEST INFLUENCE ON MY CAREER — King Kong, Frankenstein, the "Beano" Editor and Artist, my menacing Granny and Dad's slipper!

AMBITIONS — To avoid that dreaded slipper for the next five minutes!

HOW DO PEOPLE GREET YOU? — "Argh! The Menace!"